BROADWAY HITS OF THE 80s & 90s

ARRANGED FOR SOLO PIANO, INTERMEDIATE STANDARD

Exclusive Distributors:
Music Sales Limited
8/9 Frith Street,
London W1V 5TZ, England.
Music Sales Pty Limited
120 Rothschild Avenue,
Rosebery, NSW 2018, Australia.

Order No. HLE90000231
ISBN 0-7119-6437-8

Cover design by Pearce Marchbank, Studio Twenty, London
Printed in the USA

HLE
Hal Leonard Europe
Distributed by Music Sales

ANTHEM

from CHESS

Words and Music by BENNY ANDERSSON,
TIM RICE and BJORN ULVAEUS

Slow, like a hymn

mf

f
sub. p

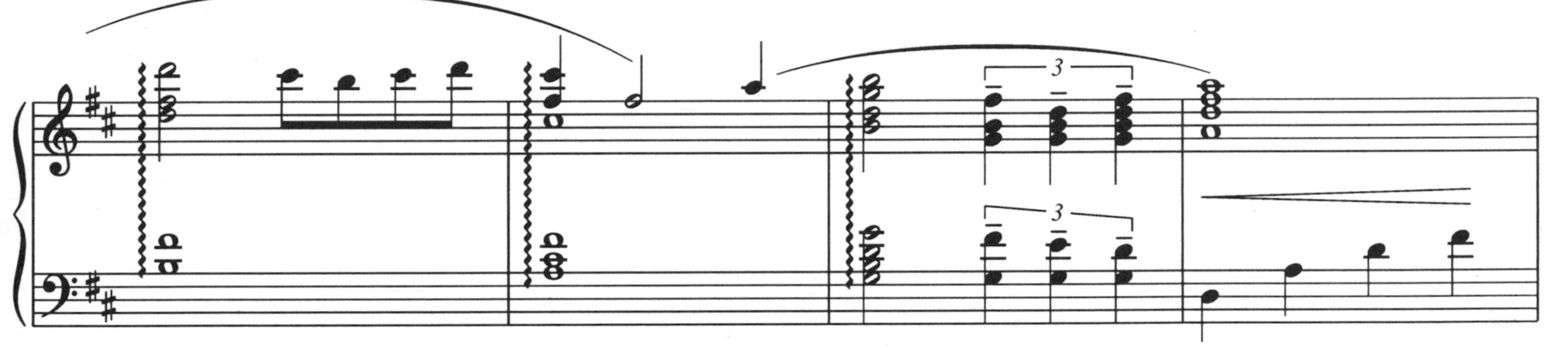
3
3

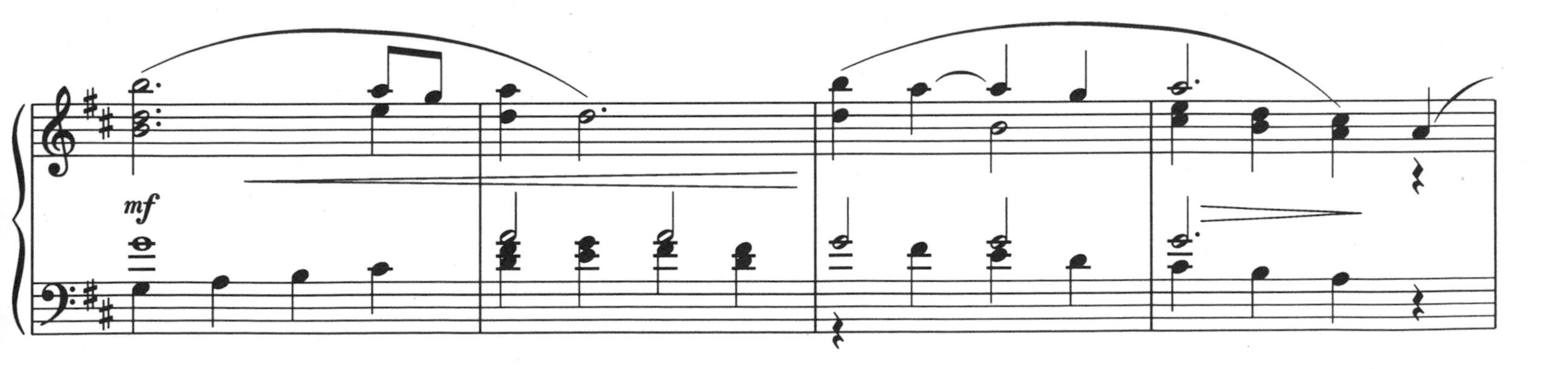
mf

mf
3

f

ff

sub. mf
rit.

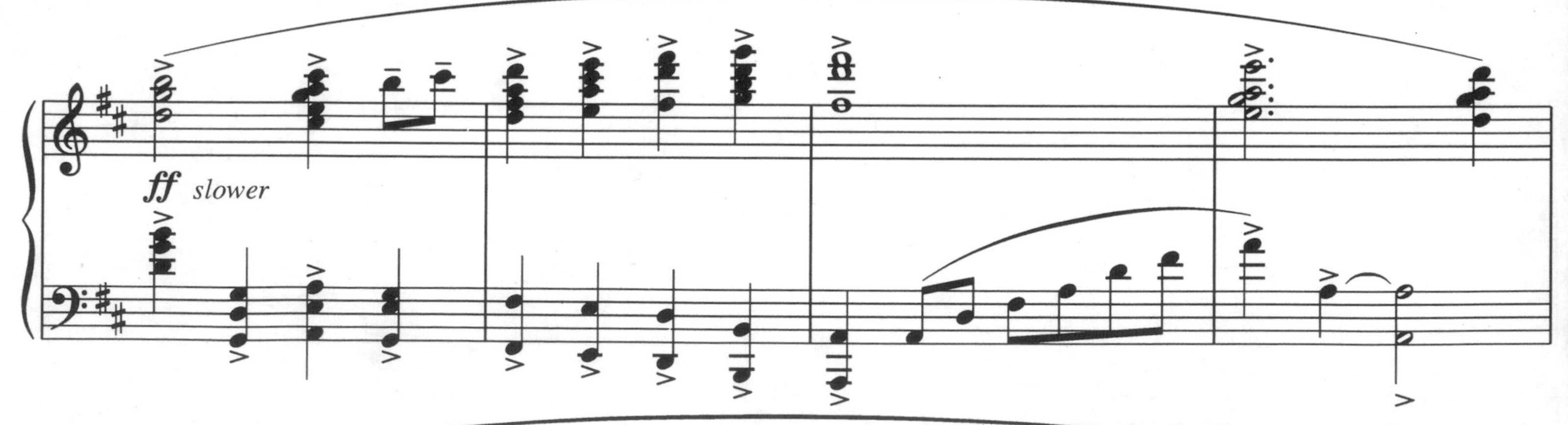
ff slower

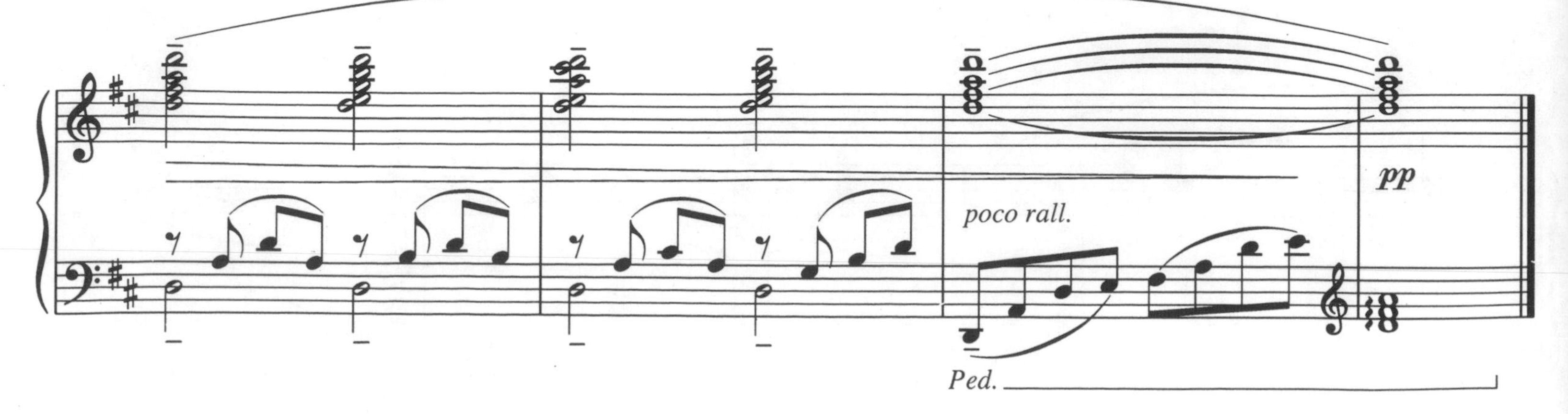
poco rall.
pp
Ped.

AS IF WE NEVER SAID GOODBYE

from SUNSET BOULEVARD

Music by ANDREW LLOYD WEBBER
Lyrics by DON BLACK
and CHRISTOPHER HAMPTON
with contributions by AMY POWERS

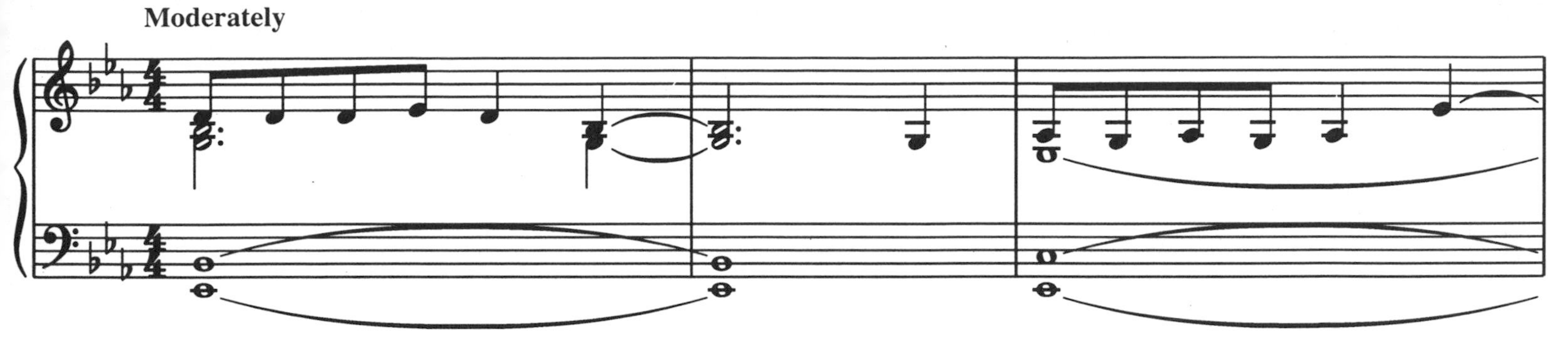

L.H.

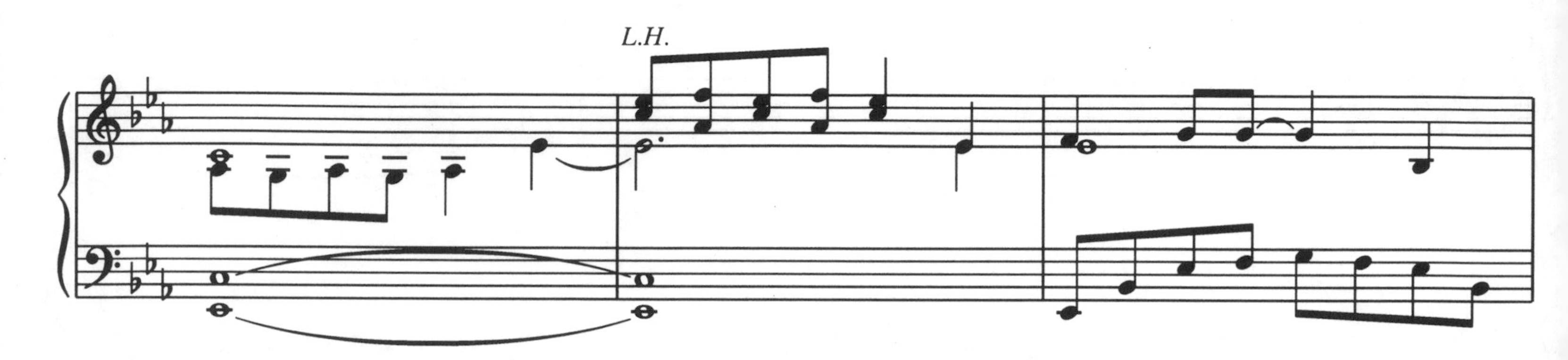
L.H.

D.C. al Coda

CODA

f

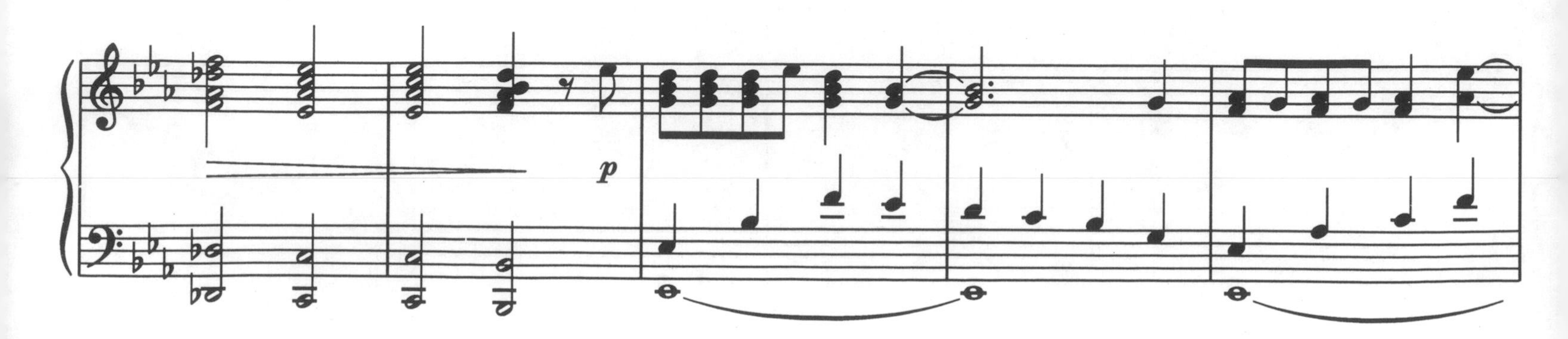
p

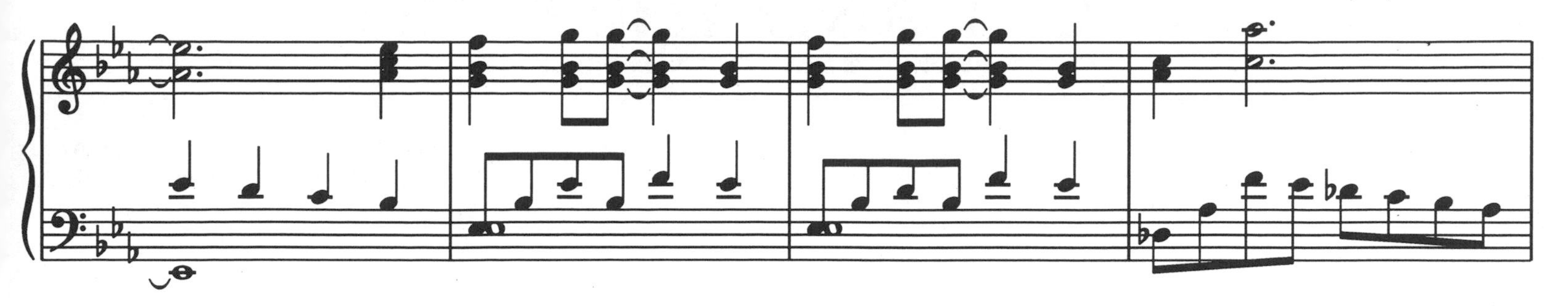

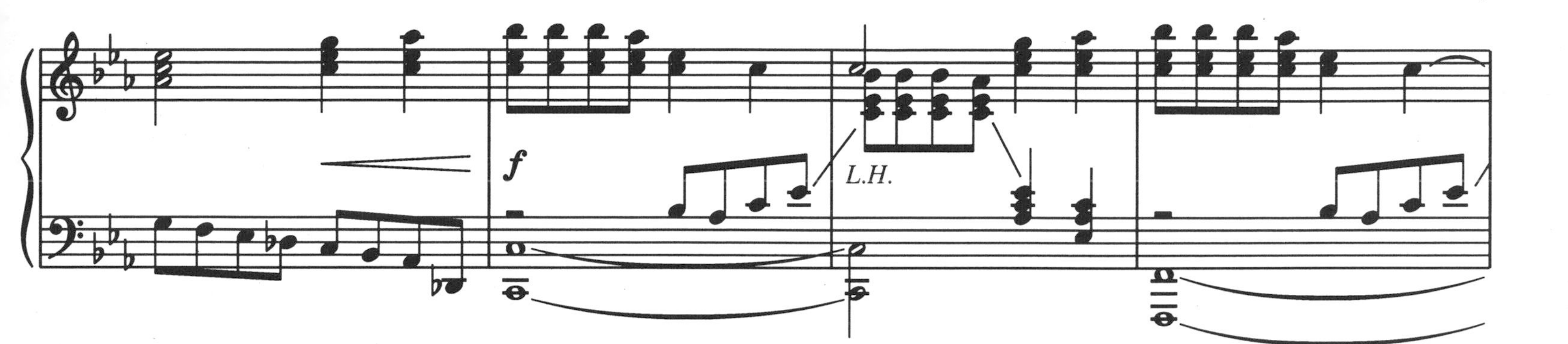
f
L.H.

L.H.

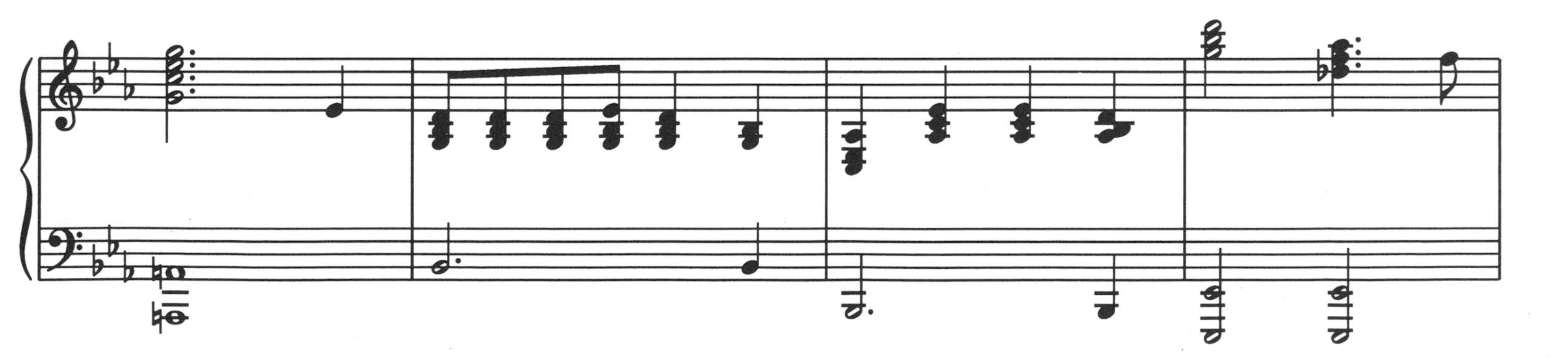

3
mp
3
f

BEAUTY AND THE BEAST

from Walt Disney's BEAUTY AND THE BEAST

Lyrics by HOWARD ASHMAN
Music by ALAN MENKEN

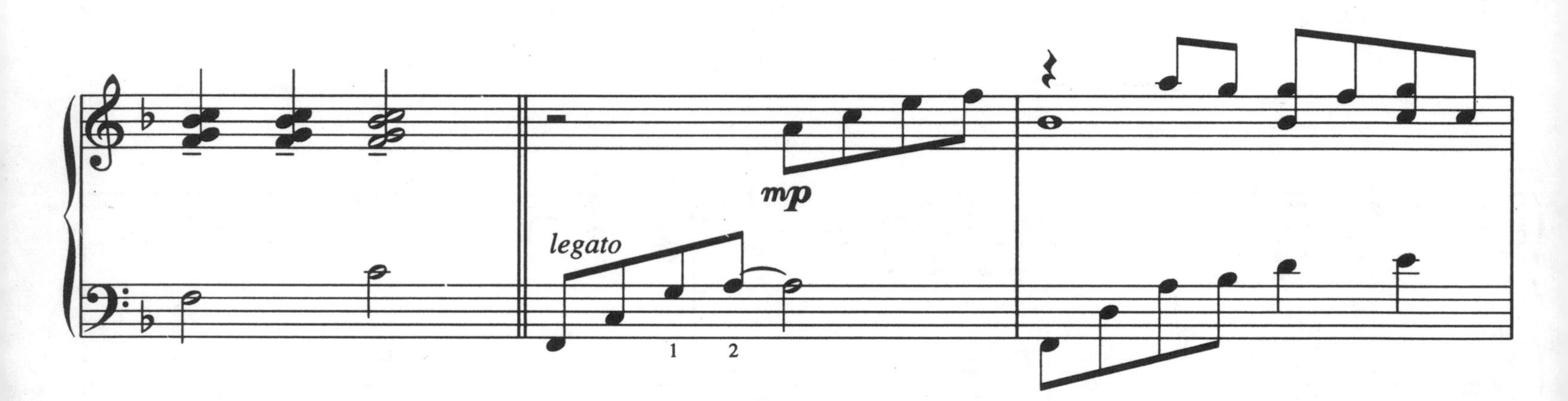

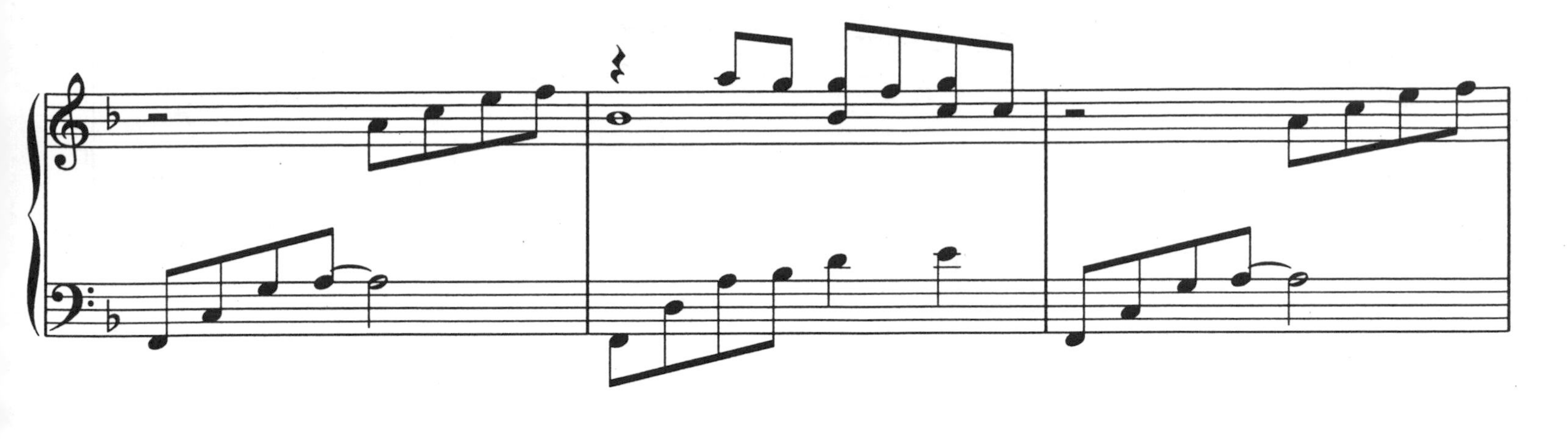

rit.

a tempo
mf

f

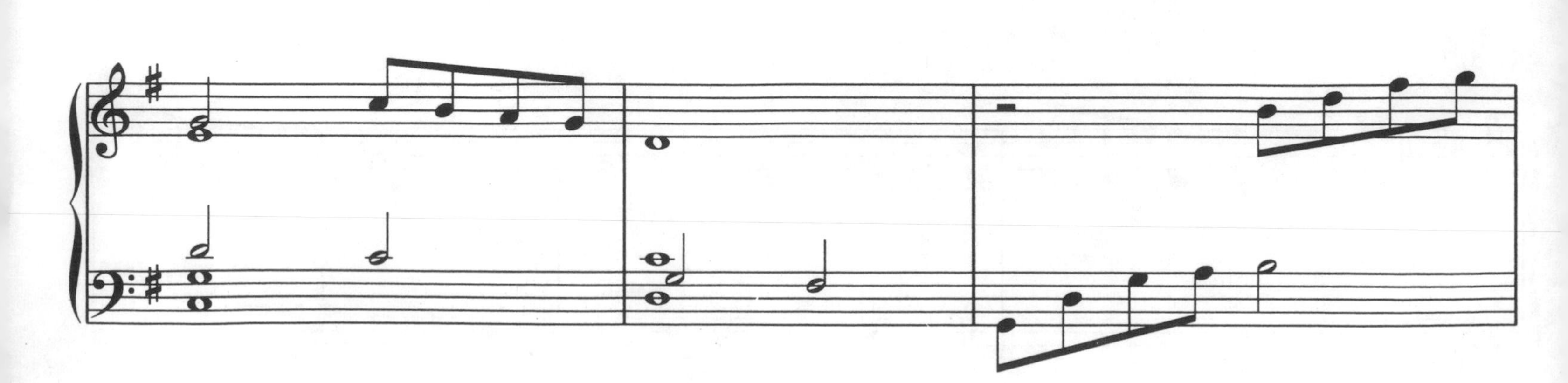

rall.
mf
a tempo

rit.

p
a tempo
4

pp
rit.

THE BEST OF TIMES

from LA CAGE AUX FOLLES

Music and Lyric by
JERRY HERMAN

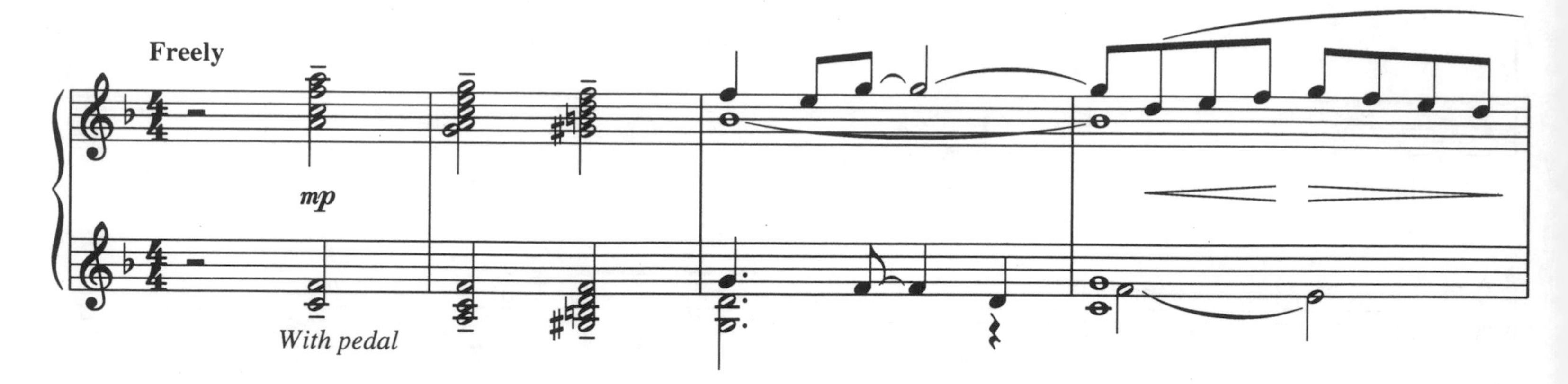

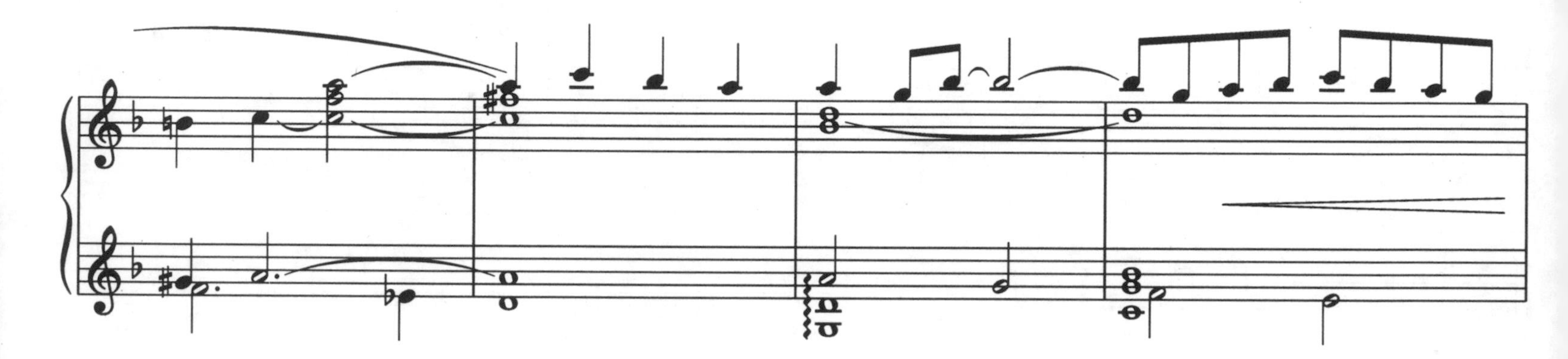

mf

p

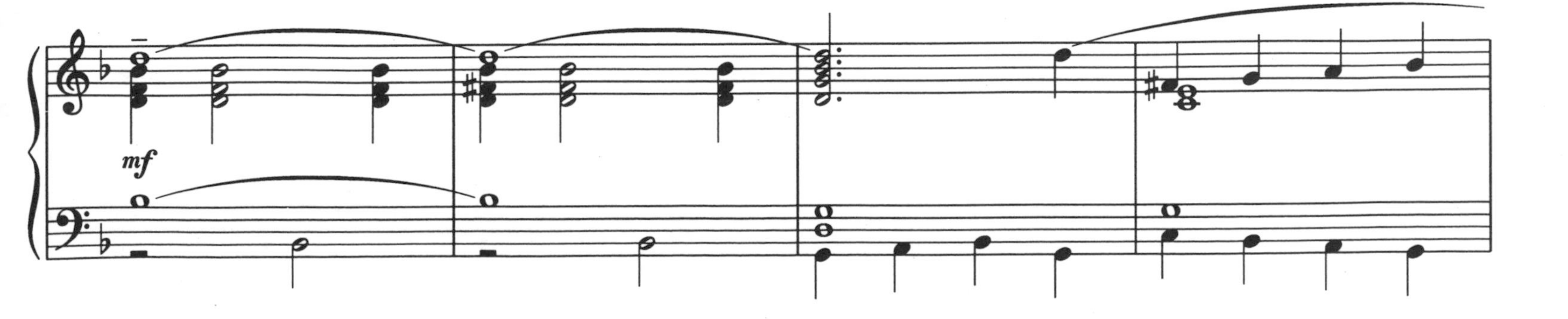
mf

sub. mp
f

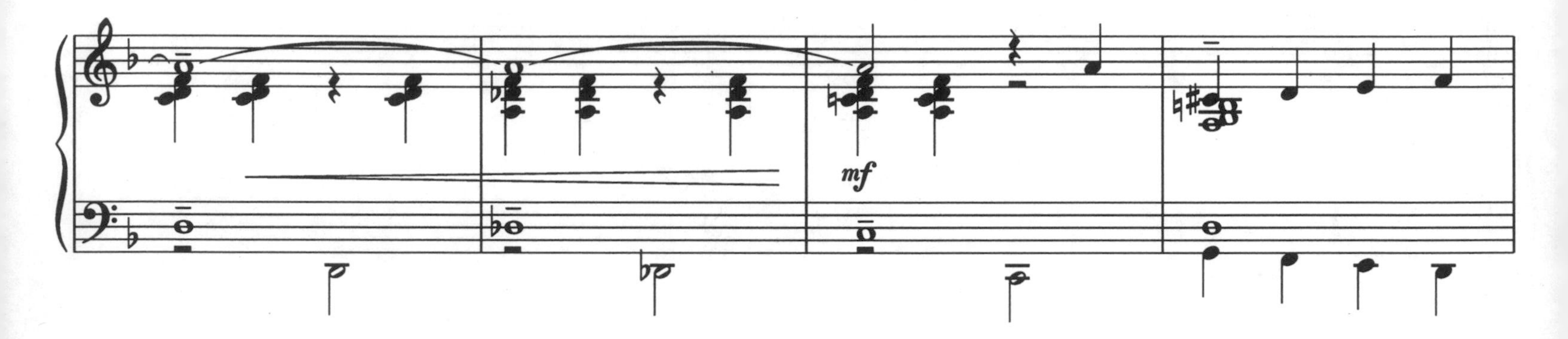
mf

f

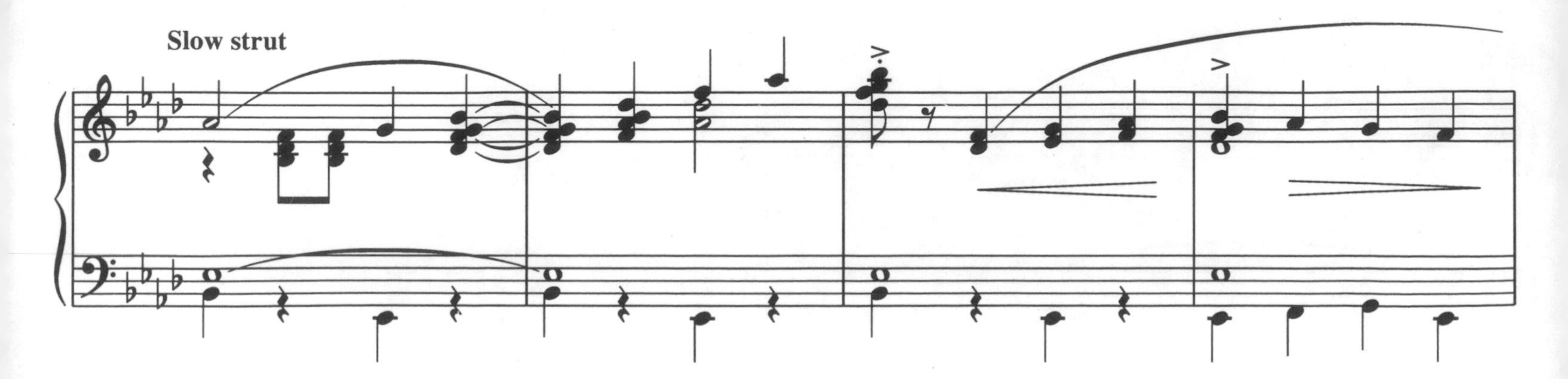
Slow strut

ff

sub. mf
f
sub. mf

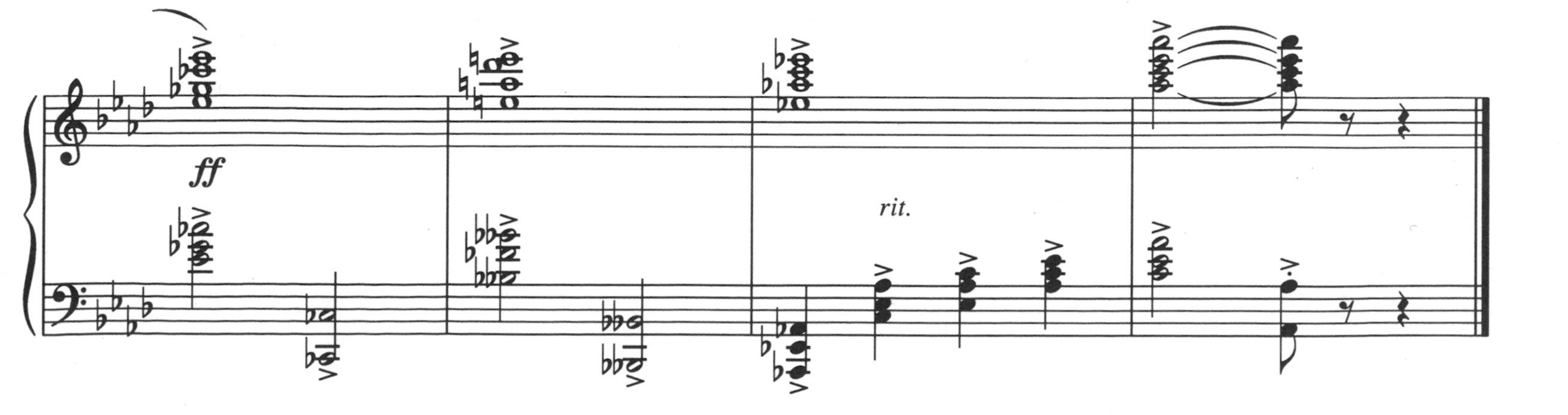
ff
rit.

IS YOU IS, OR IS YOU AIN'T
(MA BABY)
from FIVE GUYS NAMED MOE

Words and Music by BILLY AUSTIN
and LOUIS JORDAN

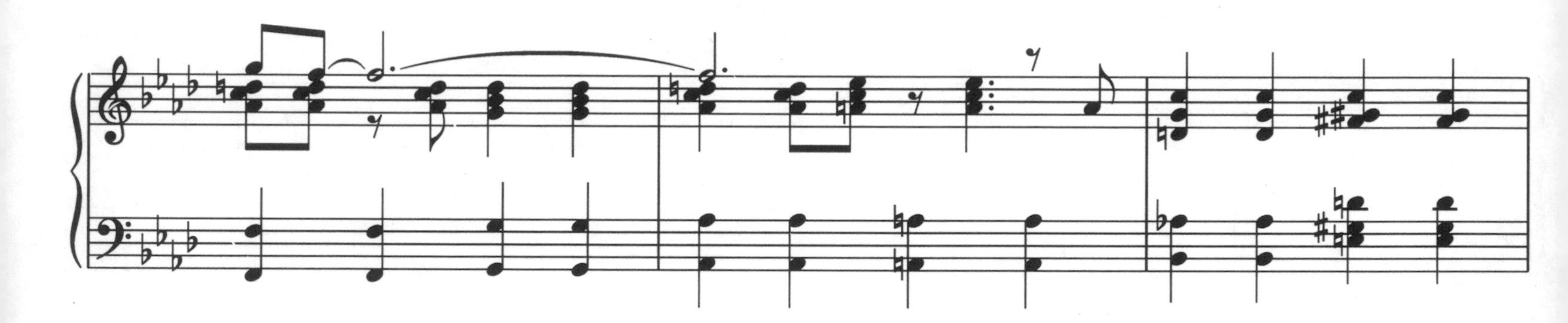

MEMORY

from CATS

Music by ANDREW LLOYD WEBBER
Text by TREVOR NUNN after T.S. ELIOT

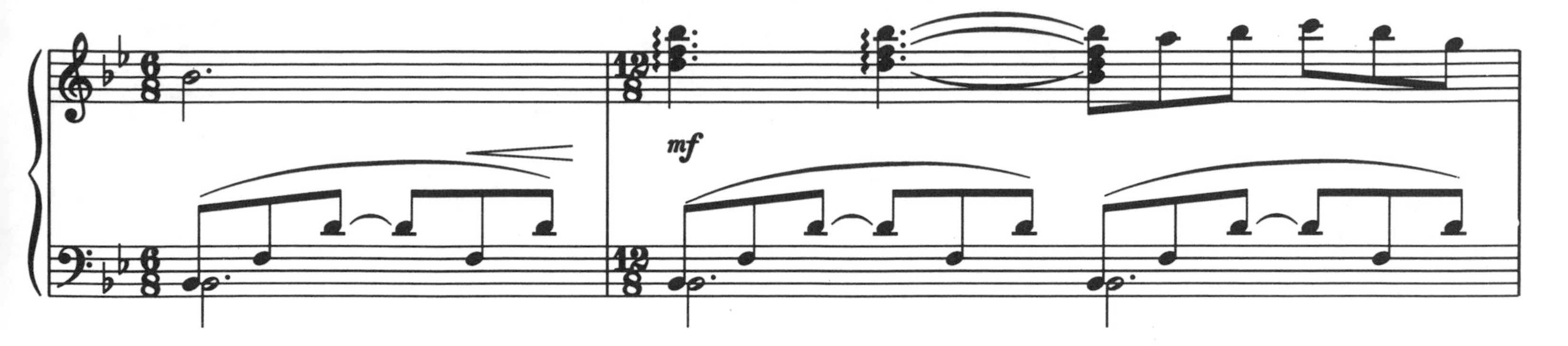
mf

p mysteriously

cresc.
mp

cresc.

mf poco rit.
mp a tempo

f

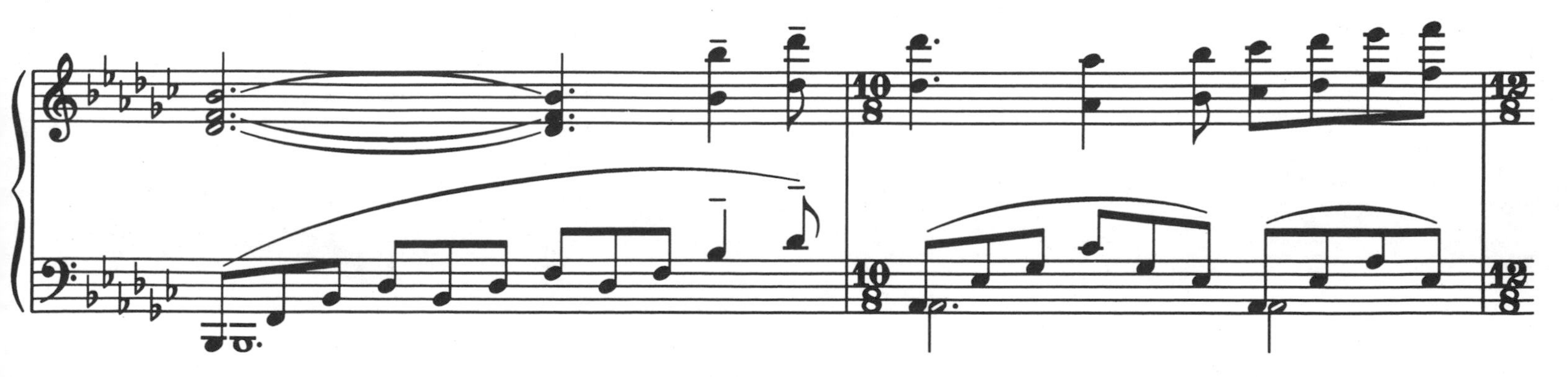

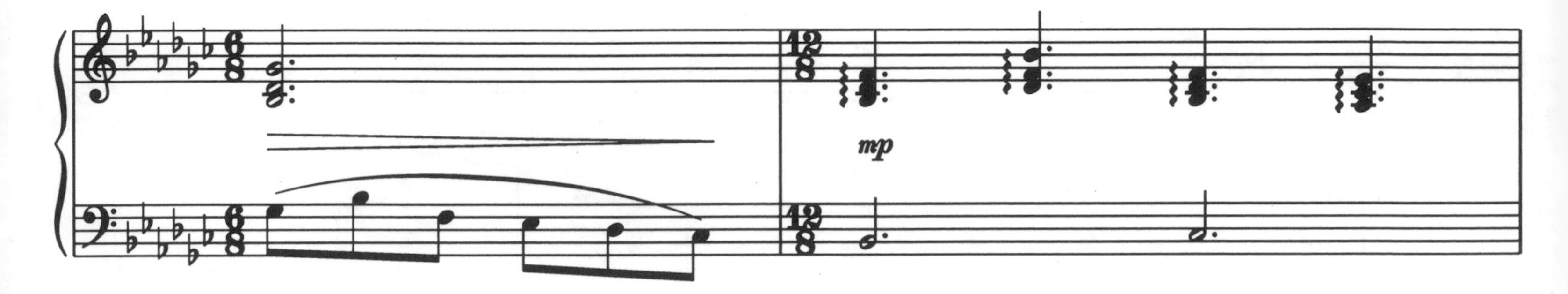
mp

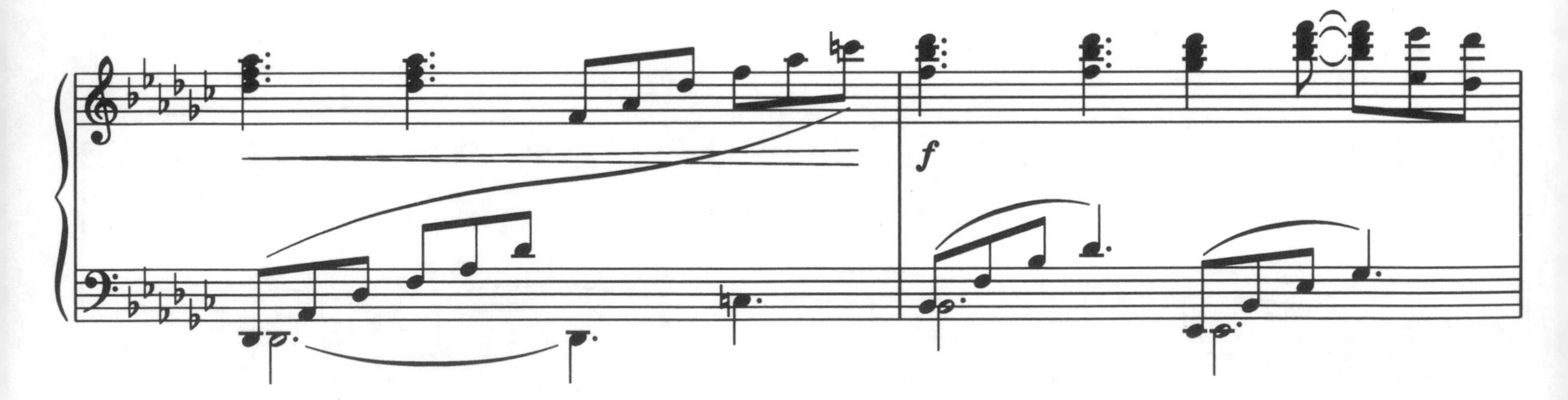
f

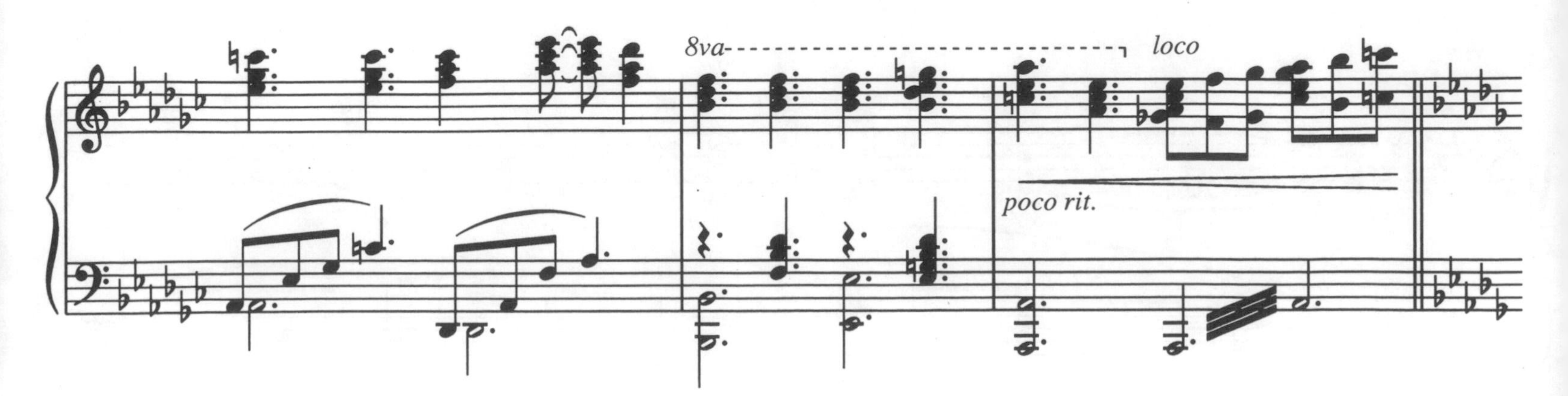
8va
loco
poco rit.

Grandiose
ff a tempo
8vb

rall.
f

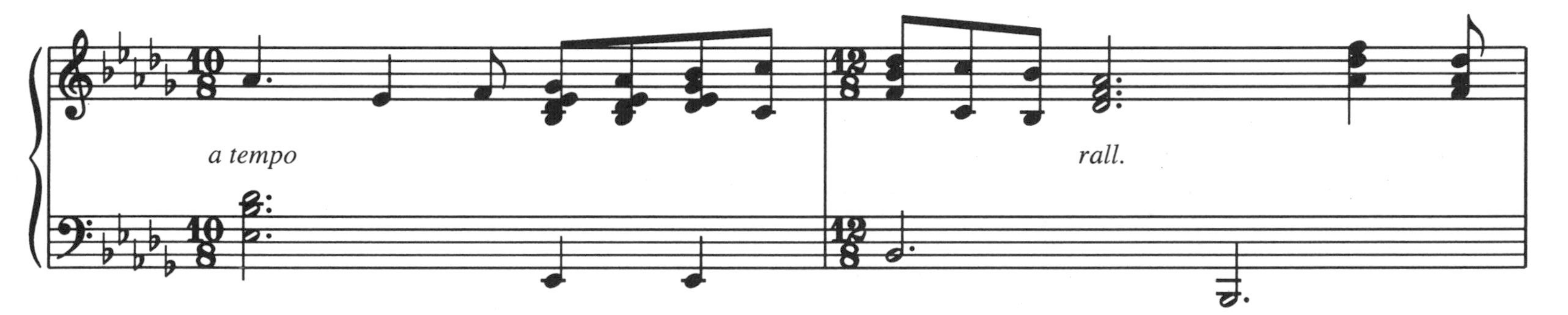
a tempo
rall.

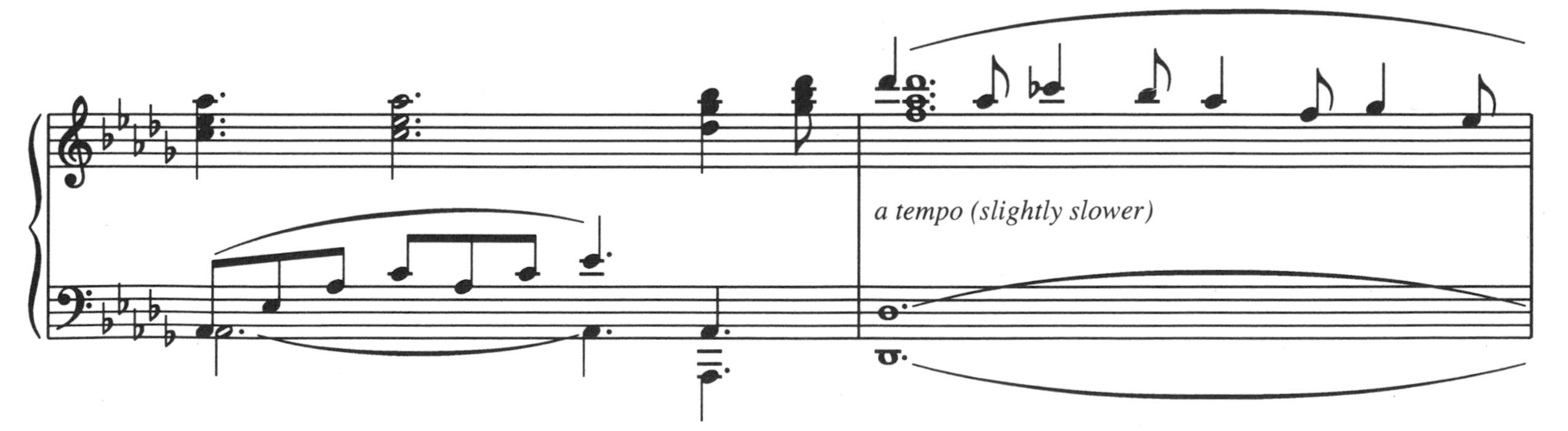
a tempo (slightly slower)

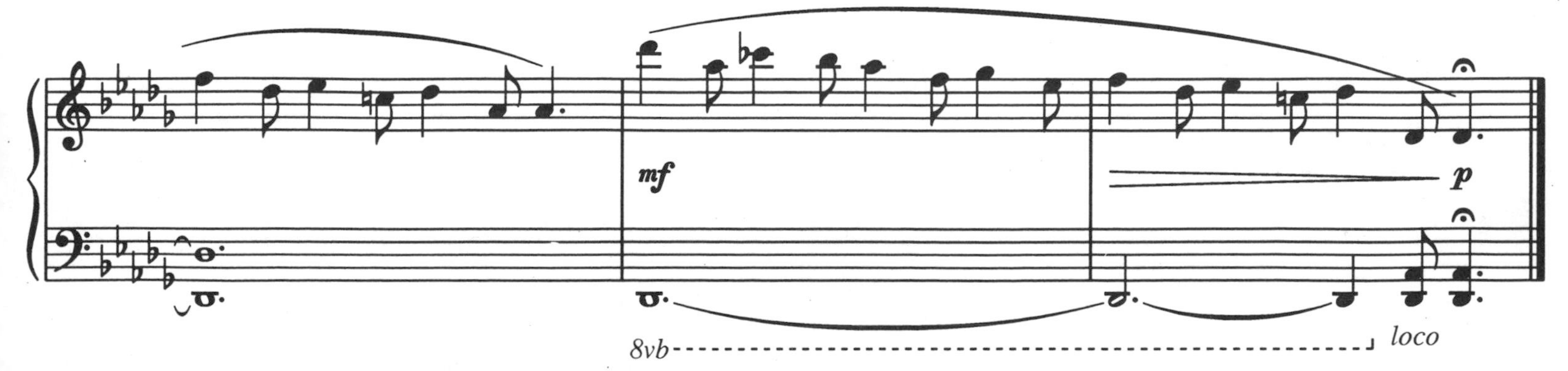
mf
p
8vb
loco

ON MY OWN
from LES MISÉRABLES

Music by CLAUDE-MICHEL SCHÖNBERG
Lyrics by HERBERT KRETZMER, JOHN CAIRD and TREVOR NUNN
Original Text by ALAIN BOUBLIL and JEAN-MARC NATEL

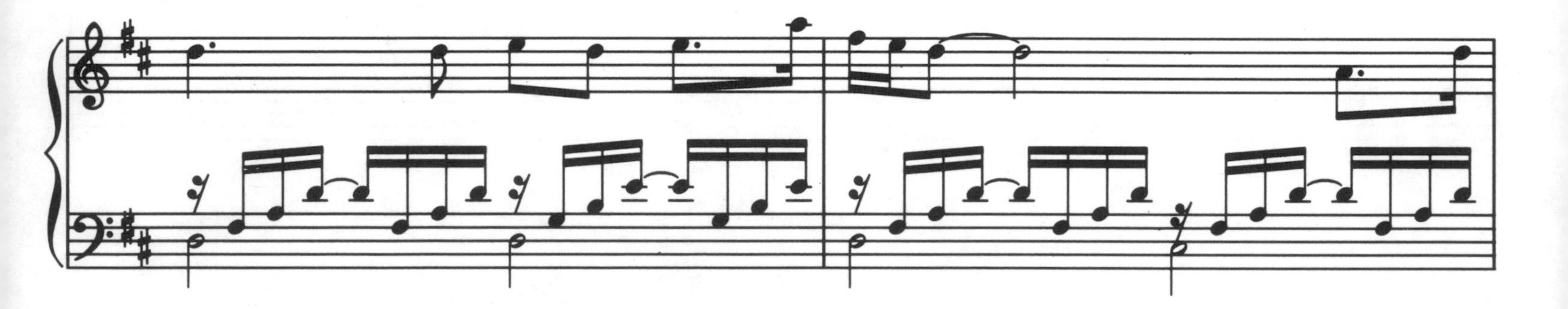

mf

mf

rall.
a tempo

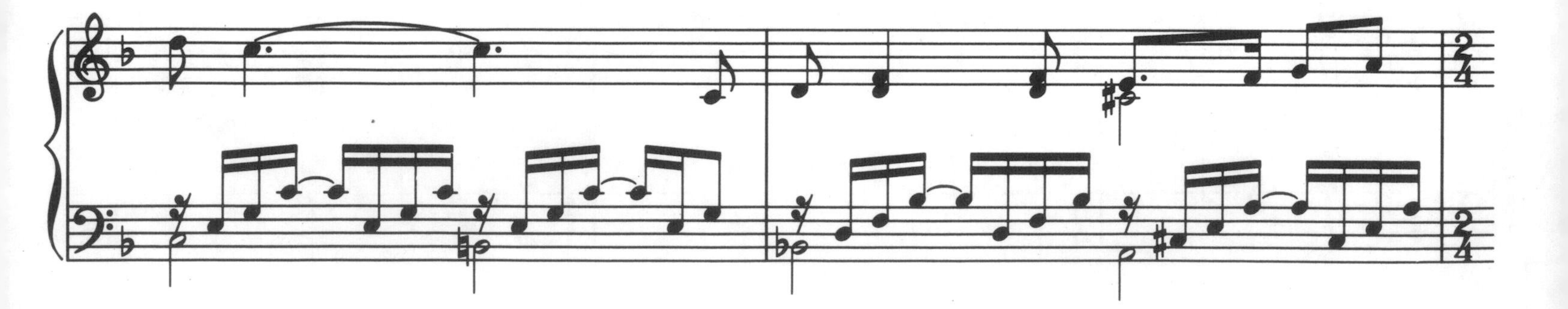

f

p

slower

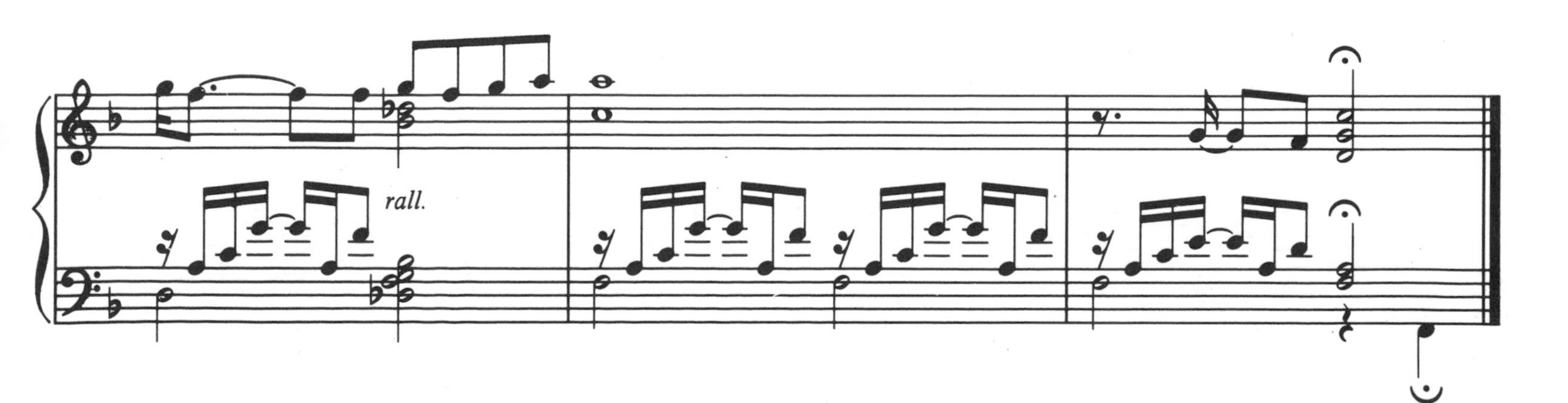
rall.

PLAY THE MUSIC FOR ME

from JELLY'S LAST JAM

Words by SUSAN BIRKENHEAD
Music by FERDINAND "JELLY ROLL" MORTON

1.

2.

double time feel

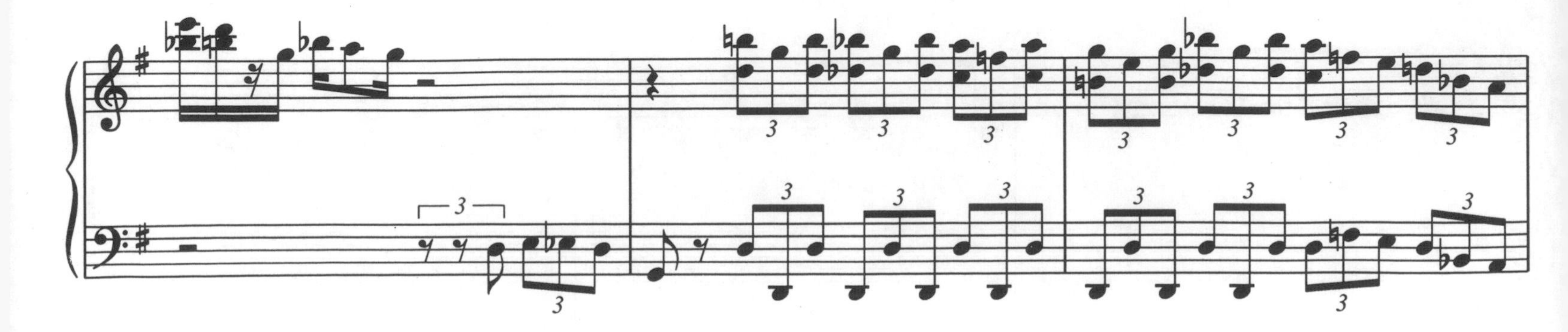

3
f

3
3
3
3
3
3

SUN AND MOON

from MISS SAIGON

Music by CLAUDE-MICHEL SCHÖNBERG
Lyrics by RICHARD MALTBY JR. and ALAIN BOUBLIL
Adapted from original French Lyrics by ALAIN BOUBLIL

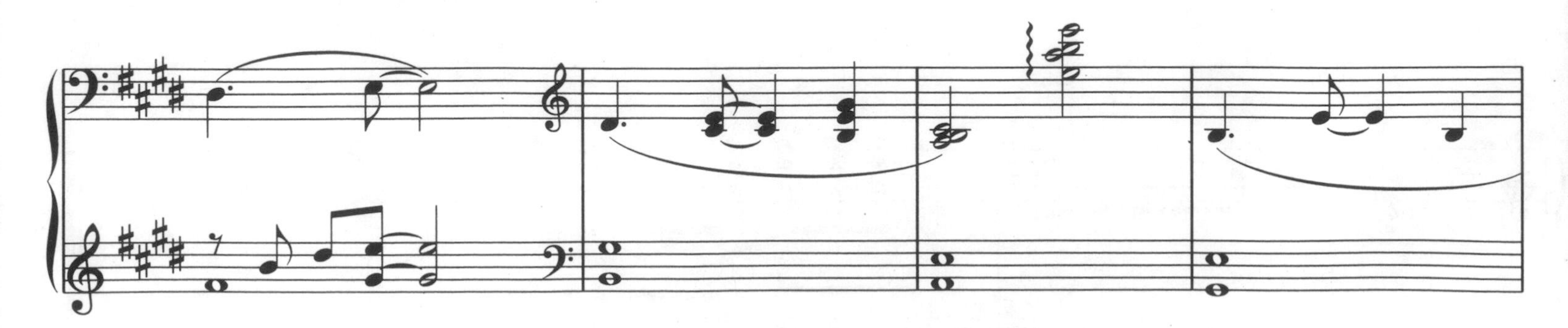

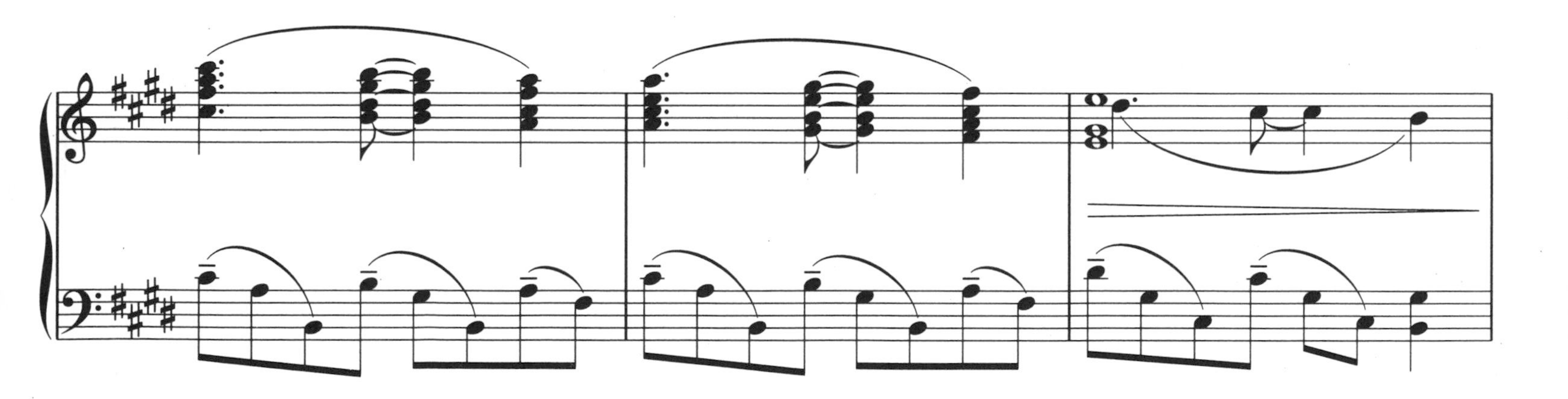

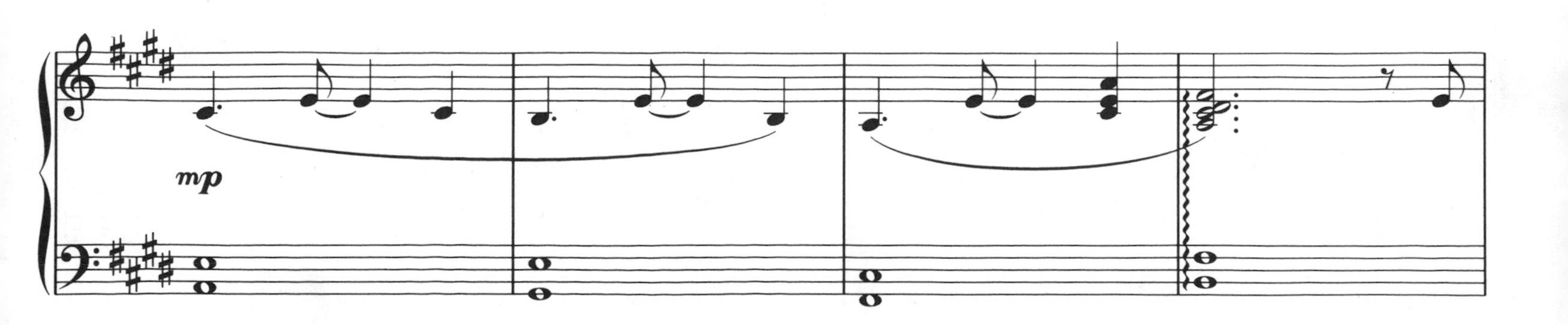

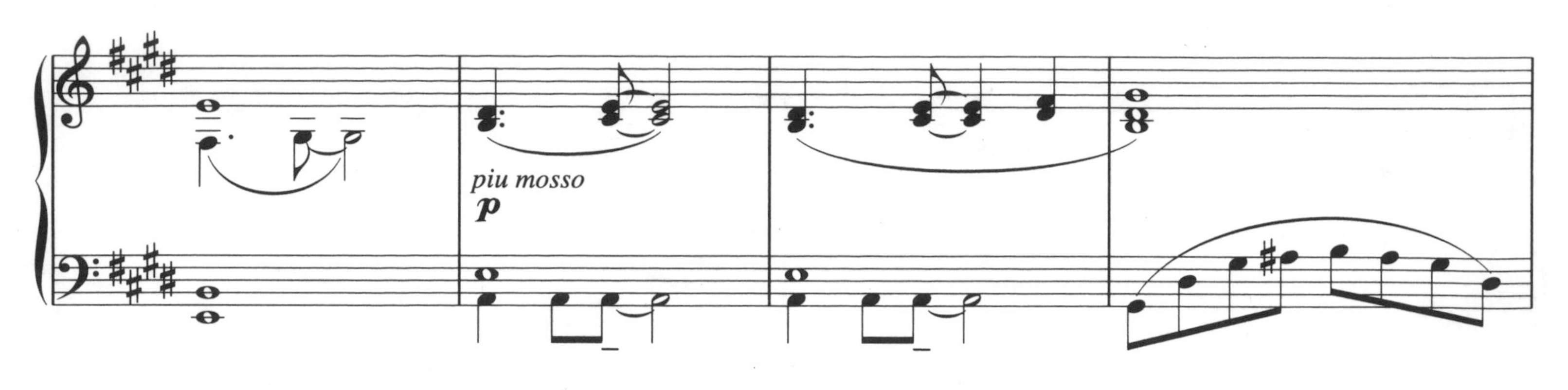
piu mosso
p

poco a poco cresc.

mf

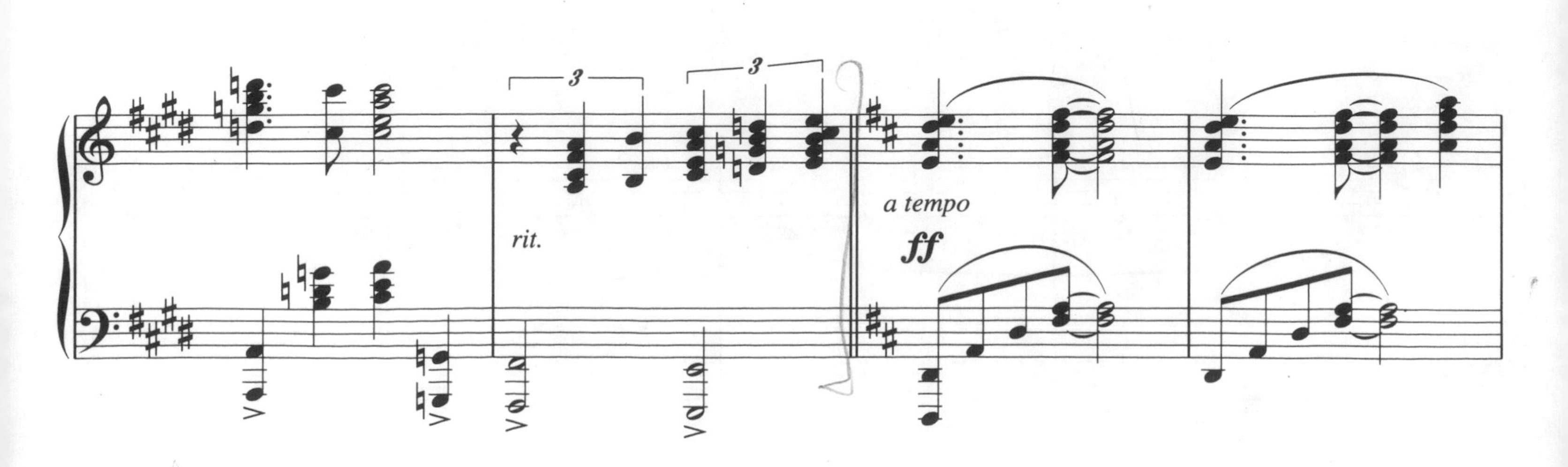
rit.
a tempo
ff

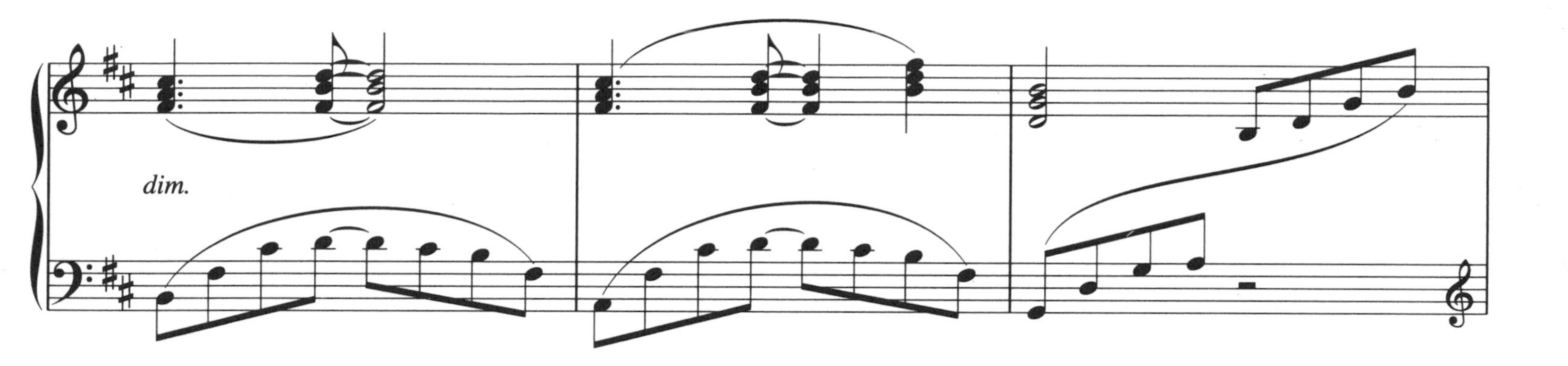
dim.

p
rall.

L.H.
pp
8va basso

UNEXPECTED SONG

from SONG & DANCE

Music by ANDREW LLOYD WEBBER
Lyrics by DON BLACK

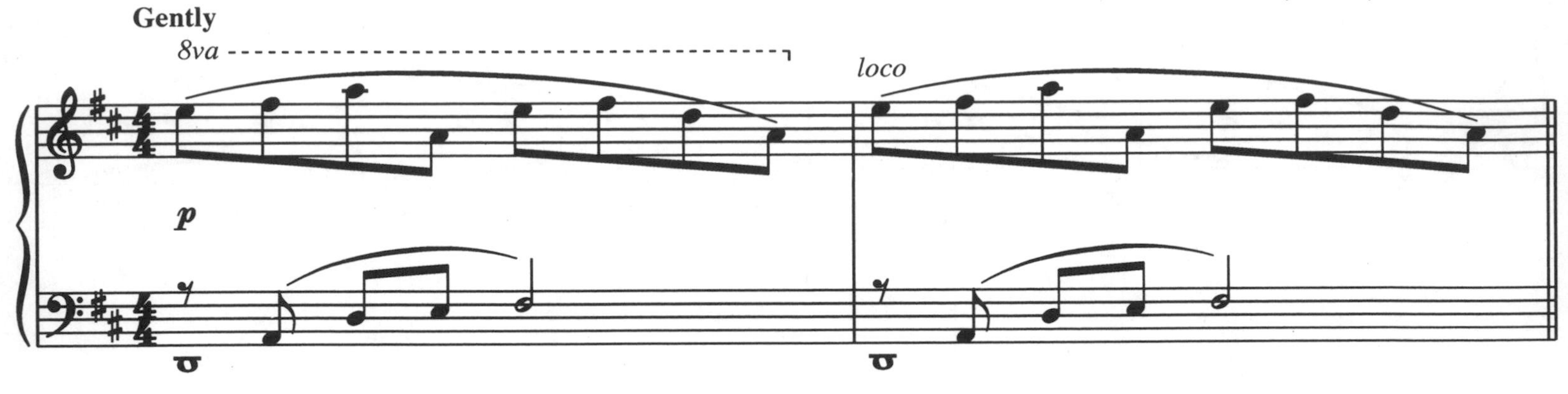

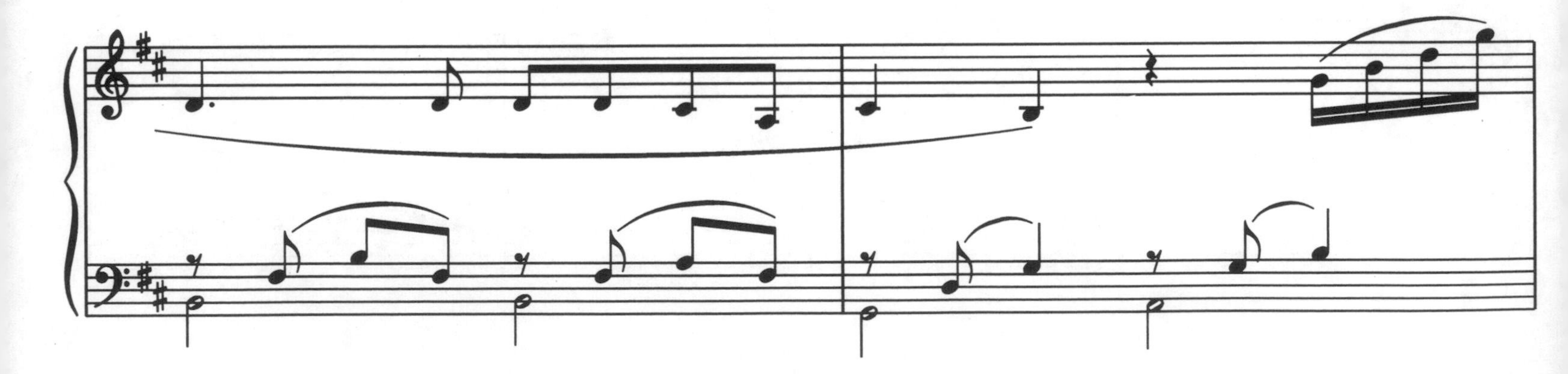

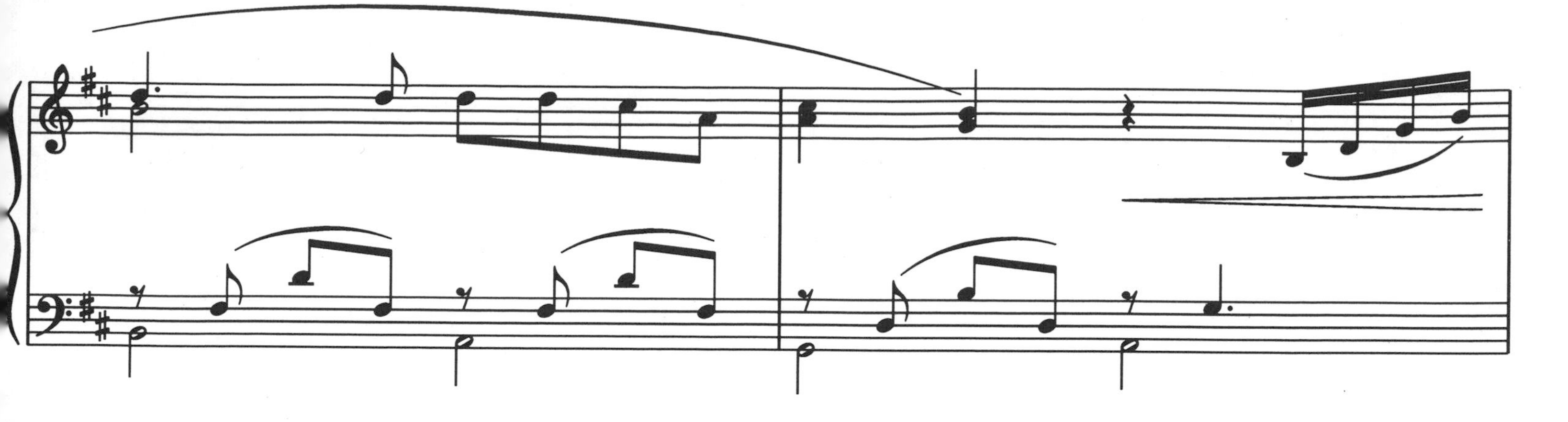

mp

1.

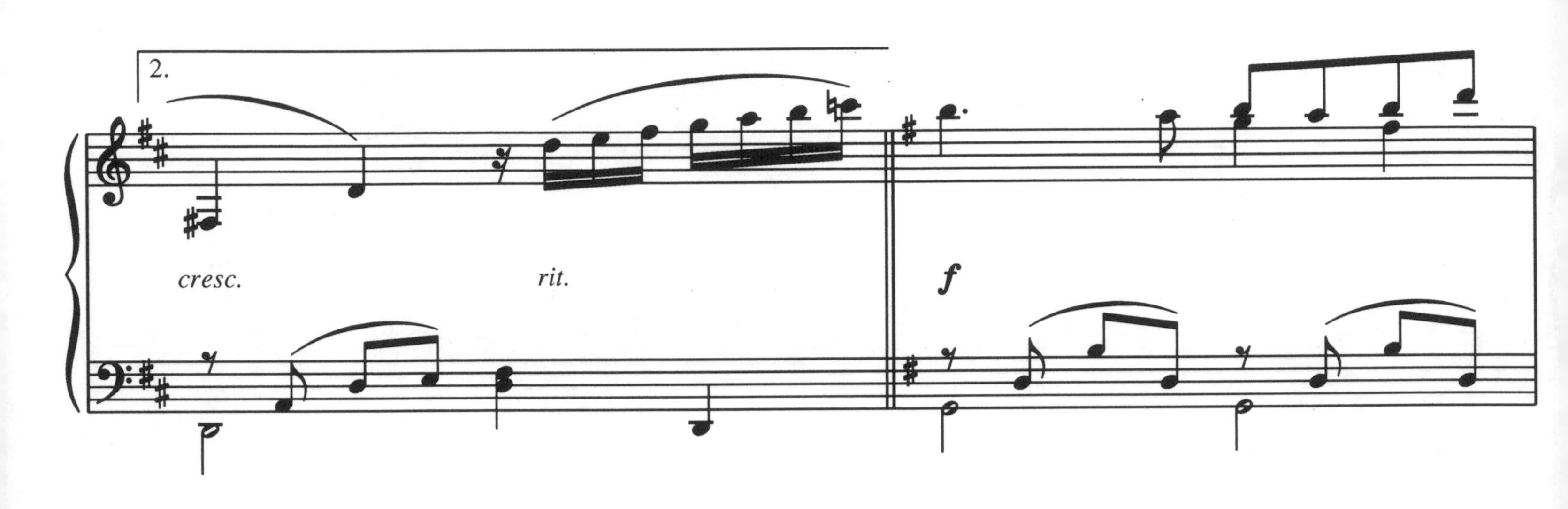
2.
cresc.
rit.
f

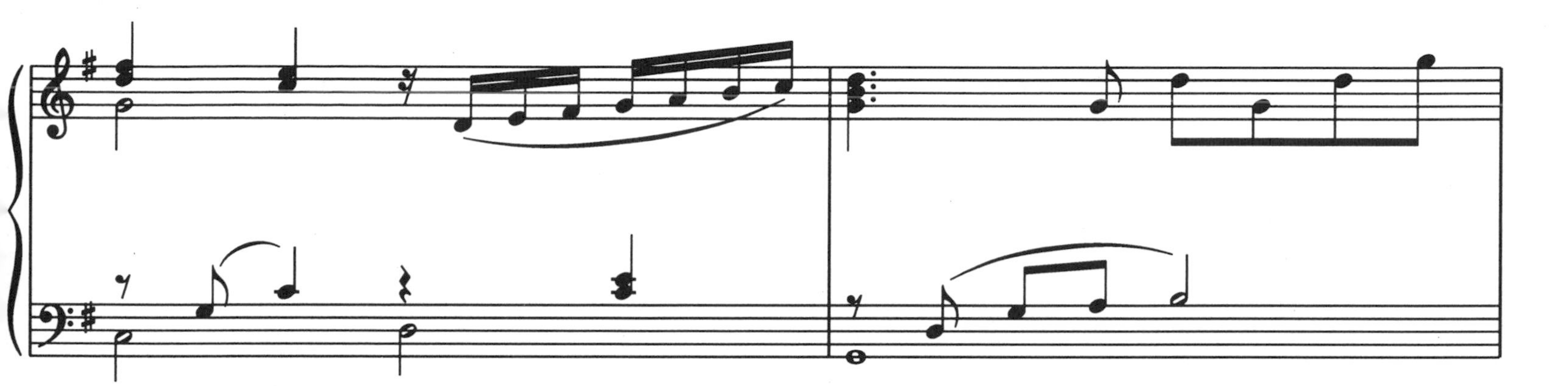

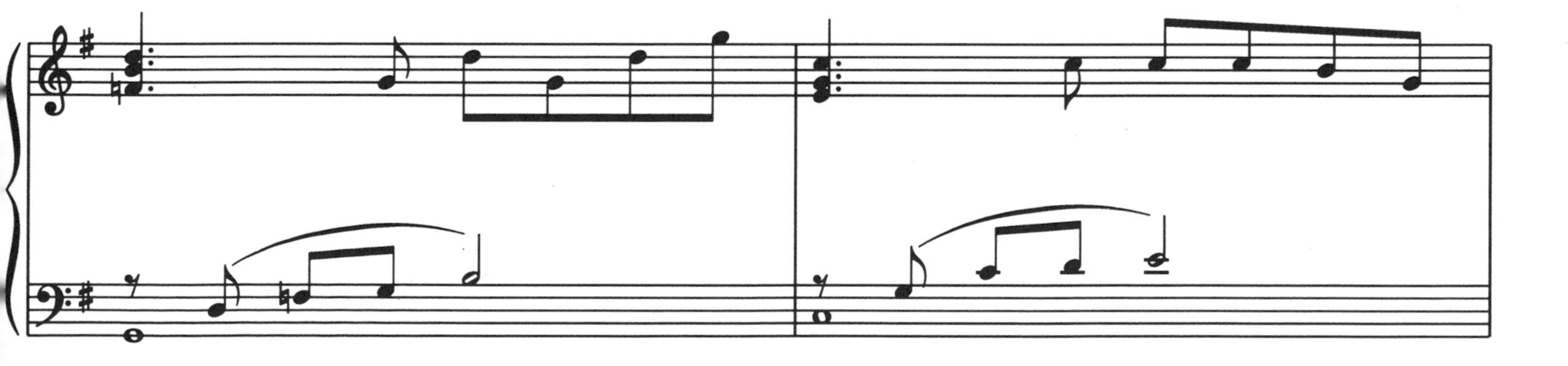

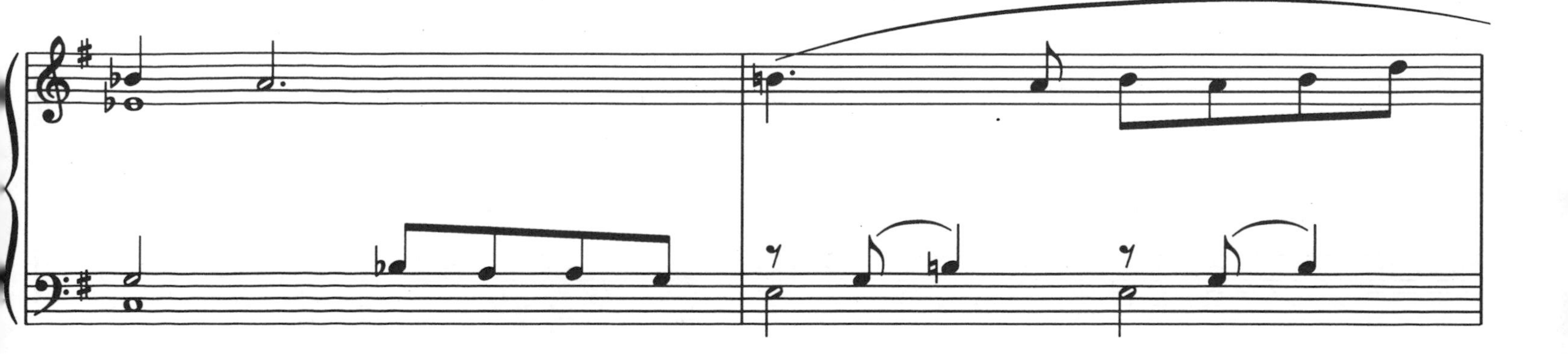

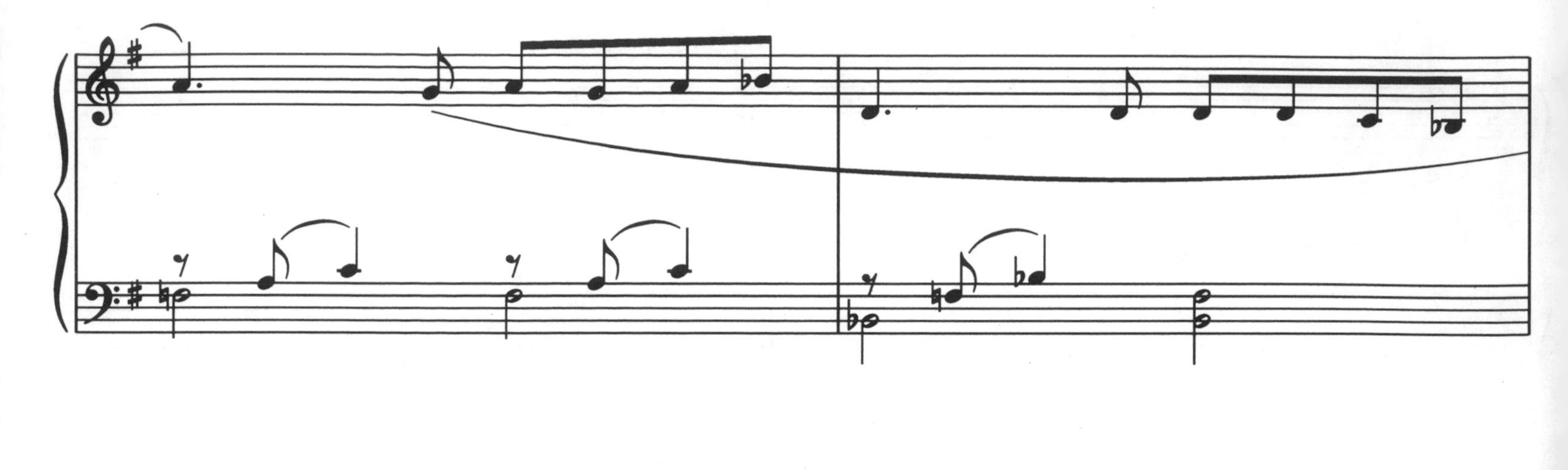

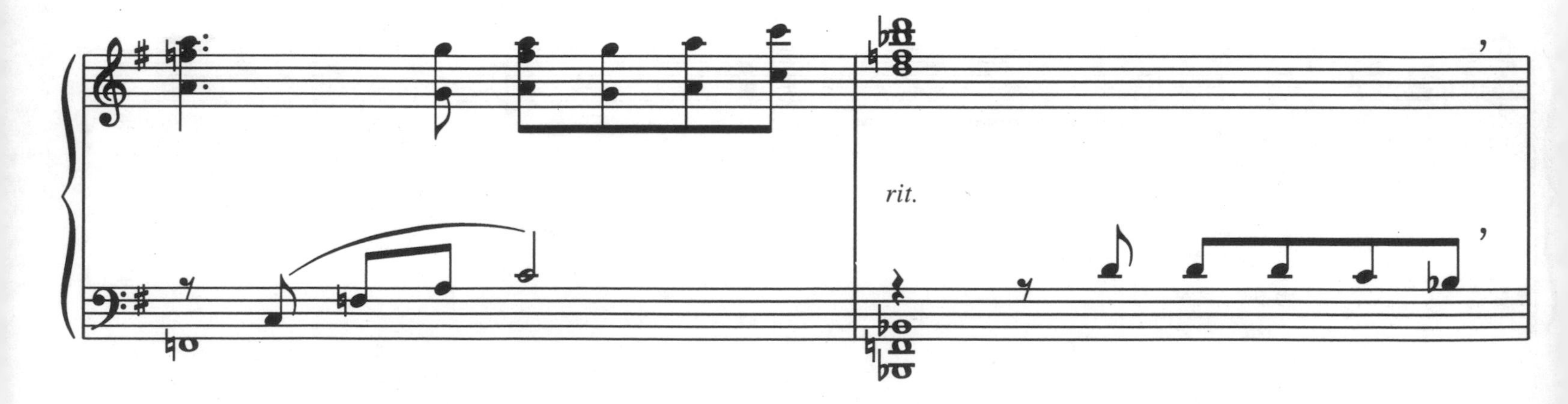
rit.

ff a tempo
fp

UNUSUAL WAY
(IN A VERY UNUSUAL WAY)
from NINE

Lyrics and Music by
MAURY YESTON

3
3

rit.

Acoustic Classics
32 songs of the 60s and 70s, including: American Pie • Blackbird • Blowin' In The Wind • Bridge Over Troubled Water • Here Comes The Sun • Leaving On A Jet Plane • Still Crazy After All These Years • Vincent (Starry Starry Night) • Where Have All The Flowers Gone? • Your Song • and more.
HLE90000011

All You Need is Love
39 songs from the hip years of the late 60s and early 70s, including: All You Need Is Love • Blowin' In The Wind • Born To Be Wild • Bridge Over Troubled Water • Hey Joe • Imagine • Light My Fire • Love Her Madly • Magic Carpet Ride • Mr. Tambourine Man • My Generation • Riders On The Storm • The Sound Of Silence • The Sunshine Of Your Love • Turn! Turn! Turn! • A Whiter Shade Of Pale • and more.
HLE90000044

Big Book of Broadway
64 songs, including: All I Ask of You • Another Suitcase in Another Hall • Any Dream Will Do • Beauty and the Beast • Cabaret • Consider Yourself • Diamonds are a Girl's Best Friend • Edelweiss • Getting to Know You • I Dreamed a Dream • If I Were a Rich Man • The Impossible Dream • Lambeth Walk • Love Changes Everything • Luck be a Lady • Memory • The Music of the Night • Ol' Man River • On My Own • Smoke Gets in Your Eyes • Sun and Moon • Tonight • Unexpected Song • With One Look • and more.
HLE90000154

Big Book of Movie Songs
66 songs, including: Airport Love Theme • Baby Elephant Walk • Beauty and the Beast • Blue Velvet • Can You Feel the Love Tonight • Chim Chim Cher-ee • A Fine Romance • Forrest Gump Suite • Heart and Soul • Isn't it Romantic? • It Could Happen to You • The Last Time I Saw Paris • Mona Lisa • Moon River • One Tin Soldier • The Rainbow Connection • Somewhere Out There • Star Trek® • Thanks For The Memory • Unchained Melody • A Whole New World • and more.
HLE90000165

The Birth of Rock 'N' Roll
37 songs with historical articles and photos; songs include: All Shook Up • Blue Suede Shoes • Blueberry Hill • Earth Angel • Goodnight, Sweetheart, Goodnight • Long Tall Sally • Rock Around the Clock • Sh-Boom (Life Could Be a Dream) • Tutti Frutti • Whole Lotta Shakin' Goin' On • and more.
HLE90000055

Imagine
30 songs for a better world, including: All You Need Is Love • Circle Of Life • Colors Of The Wind • From A Distance • God Help The Outcasts • If I Had A Hammer • Imagine • The Impossible Dream • The Power Of The Dream • Someday • Turn! Turn! Turn! • What The World Needs Now Is Love • With A Little Help From My Friends • and more.
HLE90000033

Love Is Blue
39 songs, including: Angel Eyes • Crazy • Falling in Love Again • I Should Care • I'll Never Smile Again • In a Sentimental Mood • Lush Life • The Man That Got Away • Smoke Gets In Your Eyes • Solitude • The Very Thought of You • You Don't Bring Me Flowers • and more.
HLE90000022

Shake, Rattle, & Roll
40 songs plus dozens of photos and fun facts about America of the 1950s; songs include: All I Have to Do Is Dream • All Shook Up • Book of Love • Bye Bye Love • Chantilly Lace • Good Golly Miss Molly • Great Balls of Fire • Have I Told You Lately That I Love You • Johnny B. Goode • Lollipop • Long Tall Sally • Maybe Baby • Peggy Sue • Rock Around the Clock • Shake, Rattle and Roll • Splish Splash • That'll Be the Day • Unchained Melody • Waterloo • and more.
HLE90000066

The Decade Series

Songs Of The 1920s
46 songs, including: Ain't Misbehavin' • Baby Face • Can't Help Lovin' Dat Man • Everybody Loves My Baby • A Garden in the Rain • Honeysuckle Rose • I Ain't Got Nobody • If I Had You • Louise • Me And My Shadow • Mean to Me • Miss You • More Than You Know • My Blue Heaven • Nobody Knows You When You're Down and Out • Show Me the Way to Go Home • Sunny • Who? • Why Was I Born? • You're the Cream in My Coffee • and more.
HLE90000077

Songs Of The 1930s
46 songs, including: All the Things You Are • April in Paris • Blame It on My Youth • Caravan • Cocktails for Two • A Fine Romance • Heart and Soul • I Can't Get Started with You • I'm Gonna Sit Right Down and Write Myself a Letter • In a Sentimental Mood • Isn't It Romantic? • Lambeth Walk • Moonglow • My Romance • Pennies from Heaven • Smoke Gets in Your Eyes • Thanks for the Memory • The Touch of Your Lips • The Very Thought of You • The Way You Look Tonight • and more.
HLE90000088

Songs Of The 1940s
53 songs, including: All Through the Day • Anniversary Song • Baby, It's Cold Outside • Besar Mucho • Blue Champagne • Boogie Woogie Bugle Boy • Diamonds Are a Girl's Best Friend • Don't Ge Around Much Anymore • Have I Told You Lately Th I Love You • I'll Remember April • I've Got a Lovely Bunch of Cocoanuts • It Might As Well Be Spring • It's a Grand Night for Singing • The Last Time I Saw Paris • Mairzy Doats • The Nearness of You • Oklahoma • People Will Say We're in Love • Take t "A" Train • Tangerine • Tuxedo Junction • You'll Never Walk Alone • and more.
HLE90000099

Songs Of The 1950s
55 songs, including: All Shook Up • Angel Eyes • Arrivederci Roma • Blue Velvet • Chantilly Lace • Climb Ev'ry Mountain • Cry Me A River • Fly Me T The Moon • Johnny B. Goode • Let It Be Me • Luck Be a Lady • Misty • Mona Lisa • Only You (And Yo Alone) • Peggy Sue • Que Sera, Sera • Rock Around the Clock • Satin Doll • That'll Be the Day • Three Coins in the Fountain • Tutti Fruitti • Unchained Melody • Witchcraft • and more.
HLE90000100

Songs Of The 1960s
52 songs, including: Alfie • Bluesette • Bridge Over Troubled Water • Can't Help Falling In Love • Crazy • Crying • Eleanor Rigby • The Girl from Ipanema • Here, There and Everywhere • If I Had a Hammer • King of the Road • Leaving on a Jet Plane • Light My Fire • The Lion Sleeps Tonight • A Man and a Woman • Moon River • Raindrops Keep Fallin' on My Head • The Shadow of Your Smile • Something • Summer Samba (So Nice) • Those Were the Days • Time for Us • Twist and Shout • and more.
HLE90000110

Songs Of The 1970s
46 songs, including: The Air That I Breathe • Annie's Song • Band on the Run • The Candy Man • (They Long to Be) Close to You • Copacabana • Crocodile Rock • Dancing Queen • Don't Cry for Me Argentina • How Deep Is Your Love • I Don't Know How to Love Him • Imagine • Killing Me Softly with His Song • Let It Be • Maybe I'm Amazed • Nights in White Satin • Rocket Man • Sometimes When We Touch • You Don't Bring Me Flowers • You Light Up My Life • and more.
HLE90000121

Songs Of The 1980s
39 songs, including: Addicted to Love • Against All Odds • All I Ask of You • All Out of Love • Axel F • Candle in the Wind • Don't Worry, Be Happy • Ebony and Ivory • Every Breath You Take • Hard Habit to Break • I Dreamed a Dream • Longer • Lov Changes Everything • Memory • Sailing • Somewh Out There • Sweet Dreams (Are Made Of This) • Ta My Breath Away • Up Where We Belong • What's Love Got to Do With It • The Wind Beneath My Wings • With or Without You • and more.
HLE90000132

HAL LEONARD EUROPE
DISTRIBUTED BY MUSIC SALES